Contents

Highlights®
Puzzle Buzz®

Can you find this
buzzing bee?

It is hiding 5 times
on the cover.

COVER ILLUSTRATION BY BRIAN WHITE

T5-AFD-812

Football Maze

START

Help Ned score a touchdown. Find a path from START to FINISH. If you come to a person, choose a different path.

FINISH

Hidden Pictures

Can you find these 12 items hidden in this lighthouse scene?

shoe

birthday cake

saucepan

turtle

eyeglasses

rhinoceros

scarf

kite

magnifying glass

banana

comb

arrow

Dot to Dot

Connect the dots from 1 to 22 to see someone who likes lighthouses.

5

Popcorn Search

Can you find?
Can you also find five pairs of eyeglasses?

FUN CANDY

Roll the film! Lots of people have popcorn for today's movie. Can you find 15 popcorn boxes?

ILLUSTRATION BY SCOTT BURROUGHS

Answer on page 30

Double Photo

Say "cheese"! These two pictures are a bit different. Add your stickers to the picture on this page to make them match.

ILLUSTRATION BY MIKE DAMMER

Answer on page 31

Wiggle Pictures

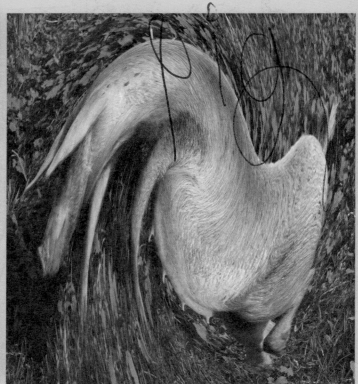

Highlights **Puzzle Buzz**

**These farm animals have been twisted and turned.
Can you figure out what each one is?**

11

Answer on page 31

Art Starters

Fill-in Fun
Color each space that has a dot to see a night flyer.

Color by Number
Use markers or crayons to color this drum.

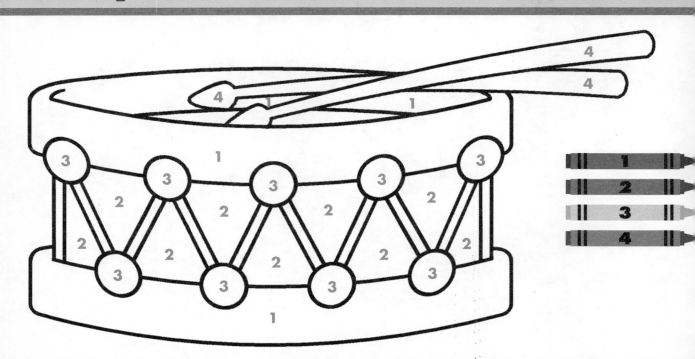

12

Step by Step Follow the steps to draw a caboose.

ILLUSTRATION BY RON ZALME

1.

2.

3.

4.

5.

Match Maker

ILLUSTRATION BY DAVE JOLY

Answer on page 31

What's Wrong?®

ILLUSTRATION BY SEAN PARKES

17

Try 10

1. Name three words that rhyme with far.

2. Name two states that begin with the letter A.

3. A rattlesnake's rattle is on its neck.
○ True   ○ False

5. Circle the vase with more flowers.

4. The Spanish word "caballo" is this type of animal.
○ dog   ○ frog   ○ horse

7. Name four animals people keep as pets.

Name three
gs you might put
a hot dog.

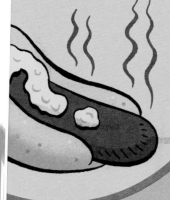

10. Circle the largest amount.

d.

Answer on page 31

Going Bananas

ZOE

ZIPPY

ZAK

eading to the playground. Find the
Who will pick up the most bananas?

ISH

ILLUSTRATION BY DAVID COULSON

21

Answer on page 32

Countdown

23

Answer on page 32

Pottery Shop

e painting cookie jars. Find all the
cker on each one.

ILLUSTRATION BY DAVID HELTON

Answer on page 32

Travel Find

There are 18 ways to get around hidden in the letters. Some words are across. Others are up and down. We found TUGBOAT. Can you find the rest?

Word List

- BIKE
- CANOE
- CAR
- KAYAK
- MOTORCYCLE
- PLANE
- ROWBOAT
- SAILBOAT
- SCOOTER
- SHIP
- SUBWAY
- TAXI
- TRACTOR
- TRAIN
- TRUCK
- TUGBOAT
- VAN
- WAGON

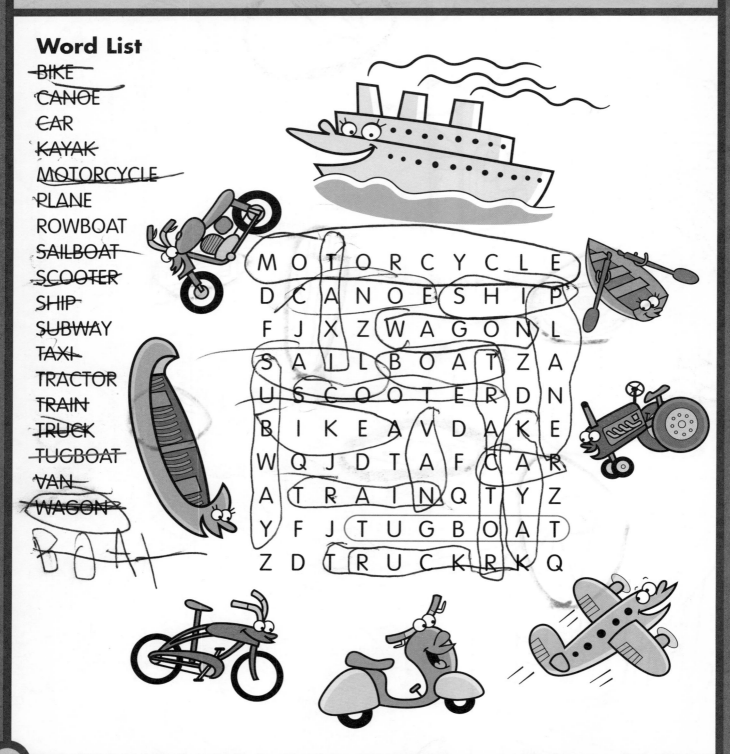

```
M O T O R C Y C L E
D C A N O E S H I P
F J X Z W A G O N L
S A I L B O A T Z A
U S C O O T E R D N
B I K E A V D A K E
W Q J D T A F C A R
A Y T R A I N Q T Y Z
Y F J T U G B O A T
Z D T R U C K R K Q
```

a poster of a place where you'd like to travel.

Answer on page 32

Fish Code

There are jokes about fish on the next page. Use the fish code to fill in the letters and finish the jokes. Then tell them to your friends!

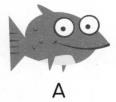

A

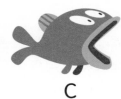

C

D

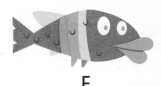

E

F

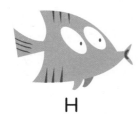

H

I

L

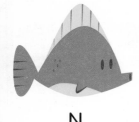

N

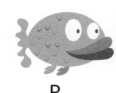

R

S

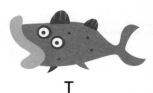

T

W

Y

are his toys?

_ E i s h .

cation?

_ h D

the most?

C a L e s

29

Answer on page 32

Answers

Cover

2. Football Maze

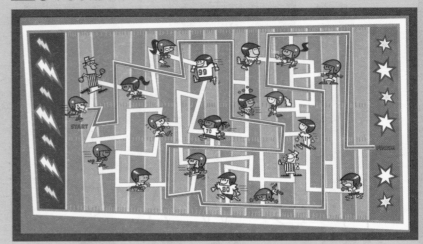

Two of a Kind

4. Hidden Pictures®

5. Dot to Dot

6. Popcorn Search

Answers

8. Double Photo

10. Wiggle Pictures

cow · goat · chicken · sheep · pig · horse

12. Fill-in Fun

It's a bat!

14. Match Maker

16. What's Wrong?®

Here are the things we found. You may have found others.

18. Try 10

1. Car, star, guitar. Did you think of others?
2. Alabama and Arizona
3. False. It is on the snake's tail.
4. Horse
5. Circle the vase and flowers on the right.
6. Fall
7. Dog, cat, guinea pig, and goldfish
8. Mustard, ketchup, and relish
9. True
10. Circle the quarter and the nickel.

Answers

20. Going Bananas

Zoe picked up the most bananas.

22. Countdown

24. Pottery Shop

26. Travel Find

M	O	T	O	R	C	Y	C	L	E
D	C	A	N	O	E	S	H	I	P
F	J	X	Z	W	A	G	O	N	L
S	A	I	L	B	O	A	T	Z	A
U	S	C	O	O	T	E	R	D	N
B	I	K	E	A	V	D	A	K	E
W	Q	J	D	T	A	F	C	A	R
A	T	R	A	I	N	Q	T	Y	Z
Y	F	J	T	U	G	B	O	A	T
Z	D	T	R	U	C	K	R	K	Q

28. Fish Code

Why didn't the lobster share his toys?
He was shellfish.

Where do fish go for vacation?
Finland

What part of a fish weighs the most?
The scales

What day do fish hate?
Fry-day

What Is It?

It's a kid holding a jack-o'-lantern!

Highlights **Puzzle Buzz**